Spelling World
BOOK 1
AMANDA GRAY

W0008717

CONTENTS

2   Introduction
4   Teaching notes

9   Handwriting Practice 1
10 Handwriting Practice 2
11 First words 1
12 First words 2
13 First words 3
14 First words 4

15 a
16 e
17 i
18 o
19 u
20 Check Tree 1

21 Handwriting Practice 3
22 sh
23 st
24 th
25 ck
26 ch
27 nd
28 nt
29 wh
30 Check Tree 2

31 Handwriting Practice 4
32 y
33 ay
34 oo
35 ee

36 ar
37 or
38 er
39 ow
40 Check Tree 3

41 Handwriting Practice 5
42 y (2)
43 ss
44 all
45 ell
46 ill
47 ing
48 ong
49 Check Tree 4

50 Handwriting Practice 6
51 Silent e
52 ate, ite
53 ave, ive
54 one
55 ake
56 ike, oke
57 Check Tree 5

58 Handwriting Practice 7
59 Days
60 Numbers
61 Colours

62 Test 1 (pages 9-35)
63 Test 2 (pages 36-59)
64-65 Record Sheet

INTRODUCTION

What is 'Spelling World'?

Spelling World is a series of four photocopiable books which (1) teaches the spelling of the most common *letter patterns* in the English language, and (2) emphasises the link between good spelling and *good handwriting*, in particular the development of a fluent joined-up writing hand.

Spelling World does not attempt to teach every word in the language, or even every word that children are likely to want to write. It does however cover some 1600 words altogether, including the 400 most common words that children use in their writing and that make up three-quarters of their written language.

Spelling World also has regular check and test pages, and teachers' notes with further vocabulary and sample sentences for assessment.

As well as the 'letter pattern' pages, there are some pages, especially at the start of Book 1, which list short words which are needed in children's writing all the time and must be learned early, though they do not have any letter string in common.

Why letter patterns?

Most words in the English language consist of recognisable letter strings or patterns which are used over and over again. Spelling World teaches those patterns, by teaching the spelling of the commonest words with each pattern. Children who can recognise these strings, understand that words are made up not of a miscellaneous collection of individual letters but of a linked series of letter patterns, and carry in their minds a visual memory of those patterns (so that they know, for example, that many words in English end with -*ack*, but almost none with -*ak*), will have little trouble in learning to spell well.

What is the method used in Spelling World?

Each page of Spelling World deals with one (or occasionally two) letter patterns. Ten words spelt with that pattern are listed, in print and in a cursive written hand (some longer words are not handwritten). The reader is asked to follow the well-known LOOK-COVER-WRITE-CHECK procedure: look hard at each word, cover it with your hand, write it in the space next to the word, take your hand away and check your spelling. After writing and checking all ten words, the pupil may turn the page over and write out again, from memory, as many of the words as she or he can remember.

It is very important to instill the LOOK-COVER-WRITE-CHECK procedure into children. In Spelling World the instruction is written at the top of each page, and in more detail in Book 1.

There is also an activity on each page designed to reinforce the learning of the letter pattern and/or handwriting practice of the letter pattern as a pattern or string, rather than as a collection of letters.

The photocopiable format is particularly suitable for this purpose as it saves much arduous and unproductive copying by children.

What is the rationale behind this method?

Spelling is a skill which depends on *visual memory*: on looking at a word, forming a 'picture' of it, and storing it in the mind. Although most good readers are also good spellers, it is not the same skill as reading, which is a more complicated thing: in fact many *fast* readers are not good spellers, because they merely 'skim' each word instead of looking hard at it. Visual memory is best developed by looking hard at a word and then attempting to reproduce it *from memory*: this is the procedure used in this series. Copying is probably of limited help in learning to spell as it does not do much to develop the visual memory.

The learning of spelling does not depend on listening, and teaching spelling by concentrating on *sounds* can be difficult and misleading, partly because so many words which sound the same can be spelled in different ways without being in any way irregular. It is probably a mistake to group words for learning which sound the same, and much better to group words which look the same, i.e. have the same letter patterns, even though they may be pronounced differently.

Of course it may be that a child mis-spells because s/he has not heard properly, and in consequence writes 'lad' instead of 'land'; but when a teacher is telling a child how to spell a word she should always write it out for the child to see, rather than spell it out verbally.

How does Spelling World work - as a sequential or diagnostic scheme?

Spelling World groups words and letter patterns roughly in order of difficulty, with regular 'check' and handwriting pages. It can be used as a sequential scheme without difficulty, and the four books should cover all the letter patterns and words needed by the average child by the age of 11, letting the individual child develop at his/her own pace.

Spelling World also works well as a *diagnostic* scheme, to help children with particular weaknesses in their spelling. The teacher may use the test sentences, test pages or 'check' pages to identify any problems a child has with spelling, and then use the appropriate pages with him/her to tackle that problem.

How do the revision and test pages work?

The revision or 'Check' pages cover the seven or eight pages immediately before them. If those pages have been tackled together as a group, their use will make sure that the patterns have been learnt, identify any problems and provide a degree of 'overlearning' - it is easy to think that once a child has got something right once they have learned it for ever! If the pages have not already been covered the Check page can be used to bring out any difficulties a child may have.

The test pages cover the whole book. They may be used as a year or term-end exercise, or to test the competence of an individual child.

What is the link with handwriting?

Spelling is also a *hand-eye* skill, and has a close connection with handwriting. Research shows that a fluent, joined-up writing hand helps good spelling, because it develops and emphasises the links between letters and groups of letters instead of treating each letter separately as print script does. Spelling World develops and practises handwriting along with spelling by offering regular practice linked to the letter patterns being learned. Spelling has little importance if the written word is illegible.

This is why most words in the word list are reproduced twice – once in print, and once in a cursive modern hand. The child learns to spell by writing from memory, and learns a good handwriting style at the same time.

(*N.B. Longer words in the word lists are not always repeated in the author's hand, in order not to cramp the space for the child's practice.*)

The handwriting emphasis in Spelling World is on learning to join up, and on developing a hand with clear ascenders and descenders the right size. These skills are helped by practising writing on lines. Books 1 and 2 use a wider set of handwriting lines, with dotted lines for ascenders and descenders, an invaluable aid for accuracy of letter height and shape.

In Book 1, all letters are written in script with joining flicks where appropriate – it helps to teach children that the 'flick' is a natural part of the letter. Joining up starts in Book 2 – at approximately the age of 8, though of course each child will be going at his/her pace and there is no 'right' age to start joining up. Books 3 and 4 promote a fluent joined-up hand, with narrower lines as hand control should be greater as the child grows older.

Each section of spelling worksheets has a handwriting practice sheet preceding it, so that children can practise the letter patterns before they concentrate on learning the spellings.

What is the link with the National Curriculum?

Spelling and handwriting are part of Attainment Target 3: Writing.

At Key Stage 1 children should be taught to write each letter of the alphabet, learn simple spelling patterns, spell commonly occurring simple words, and use simple morphemes (un-, in-, -ed, -ing). The Programme of Study specifies that close attention should be paid to word families, and that children should learn to use word books and dictionaries to check for spelling. Children should be learning comfortable, legible handwriting, writing from left to right and top to bottom, with a regular size and shape of letters, and a regular spacing of letters and words. They should also be learning the conventional ways of forming letters, both upper and lower case.

At Key Stage 2 children should be forming a bank of words which they can spell; they should be learning to check spellings in a dictionary and to understand dictionary conventions. They should learn to use and spell common prefixes and suffixes, to use apostrophes correctly, to recognise silent letters, *to memorise the visual patterns of words* and to know the terms vowel, consonant etc. In handwriting children should develop fluent and legible handwriting, joined up and printed, and understand the use of different styles and handwriting for different purposes.

Some do's and don'ts

Do:

Encourage children to take an interest in words and how they are formed. Point out similarities between words.

Try to make children write from memory rather than copy.

When a child asks how to spell a word, write it out rather than spell it out.

Encourage spelling games.

Always use the procedure LOOK-COVER-WRITE-CHECK.

Praise good spelling and respond positively to attempts to spell words.

Encourage children to check their own work.

Don't:

Don't tell a child s/he is a bad speller. Children told this will believe it.

Don't criticise a child's writing with regard only to spelling. Writing is not primarily about spelling. If children think they will be judged by their spelling, they may end up as reluctant writers.

Don't sound out words they want to spell. Sounds can be very misleading.

Don't spell out a word letter by letter. Write out the whole word.

And remember:

* Spelling is a different skill from reading. A good reader is not necessarily a good speller.

* Spelling and handwriting are not indicators of intelligence. Numerous bad spellers become good writers!

* Spelling is developmental. Children do not all grow at the same rate at the same time.

Teaching Notes

Extension words and test sentences

Read out the whole sentence to the child. Ask him/her to write only the word in *italics*.

11   First words 1

1 Please share *your* book with *me*.

2 Look at *the* little mouse *and* the big cat.

12   First words 2

1 It is raining *so* put on your coat.

2 Do not *go to* the shop by yourself.

13   First words 3

1 Come and sit *by* me *on* the bench.

2 How many pencils *have* you got?

14   First words 4

1 Will you *come* to my party *at* my home?

2 Who *has* seen *his* books? Please give them back to *him*.

15   a

mad pad sad rag wag cap lap map tap ham jam Pam fan pan van bat pat sat glad

1 The *cat* is *fat* because it eats too much.

2 Mum and *Dad ran* to catch the bus.

16   e

fed led Ted wed Ben den hen pen bet jet net pet set met beg

1 *Red* is the colour for danger.

2 *Let* me help you *peg* out the washing.

17   i

fig pig jig wig bin din fin pin sin tin win rid lid him rim dip hip pip sip bit hit lit pit wit mix

1 That *big* jigsaw piece will *fit* in there.

2 How *did* you learn to swim?

18   o

bob hob job lob mob rob sob mop pop bog cog fog hog jog cot dot jot pot rot tot

1 My cake is burnt because it *got* too *hot*.

2 Put the *top* back on the *box*.

19   u

bun fun gun nun pun cut gut hut nut rut jut pup sup bud dud mud bug dug hug hug mug pug rug tug rub tub pub

1 Add *up* the *sum* of three and four.

2 *Mum* gave me a *cup* of tea.

22   sh

shoe show short shoot shook sharp shake shade shape shall shell sheep shelf crush brush rush ash dash rash sash crash flash mash smash

1 *She* went to buy some *fish*.

2 Please *shut* the *shed* door.

23   st

mast lest test vest west rest list mist fist host most frost chest dust rust start stamp stun stub stand stoop stool steal steel stiff step stop castle master

1 I have *lost* my favourite pen.

2 The *last post* goes at five o'clock.

24   th

there those thick bath path both with father mother brother rather

1 *They* walked along the *path.*

2 I *think that* it is going to snow.

25 ck

pack lack rack tack sack track smack slack lick tick chick quick trick thick sock lock rocket stock shock frock flock deck peck muck suck tuck bucket cluck stuck

1 The *clock* stopped at one.

2 *Pick* a number which brings you *luck.*

26 ch

chap chair chum chump church chimp chill chimney child each teach bunch lunch catch watch witch hitch latch batch patch

1 If you *chat* too *much* you will miss the story.

2 Each *child* can have some *chips.*

27 nd

band land sand wand stand bend fend lend mend tend bind hind kind rind fond second window friend island bandage tender sandal

1 A frog lives in the *pond.*

2 Look *under* the stone and you will *find* a worm.

28 nt

rant giant plant infant lint pint tint winter dent enter spent absent present twenty plenty punt runt student until front month

1 We *lent* our *tent* to our friends.

2 I *want* some *mint* chocolate.

29 wh

whale wheat whine whip whisk whiz whole whoop nowhere somewhere

1 *Which* of these coats is yours?

2 Wear your *white* goggles *when* you swim.

32 y

dry fry guy shy sly spy sty reply

1 I want to *fly* in the *sky* like a bird.

2 When you *buy* sweets, they are *by* the door in the shop.

33 ay

bay hay jay lay ray tray pray fray clay display always delay pay repay dismay

1 *Yesterday* was Tuesday, so *today* is Wednesday.

2 I *may play* football after school on Friday.

34 oo

good mood cook hook cool pool tool wool moon noon loop hoof loom boot foot root shoot hoot tooth floor spoon gloom bloom stool school shook stood flood blood wooden room

1 Here is a *book* about *zoo* animals.

2 The *poor* man walked through the *wood.*

35 ee

been seen need weed seek feel heel peel reel wheel steel needle teeth sleep green queen keep deep peep

1 One and two make *three.*

2 I'll *meet* my friends under the oak tree.

36 ar

are ark art cart dart part tart start smart chart bar jar tar hard lard ward yard barn darn warn army harm warm charm harp sharp shark spark scar scarf lark mark march large

1 *Park* the car at the *farm.*

2 The *star* shone brightly in the *dark* sky.

37 or

cord ford lord word bore core fore more sore tore wore cork fork pork York sport snort stork horn torn worn form worm storm port short forth north horse

1 What *sort* of *story* do you like best?

2 We went *for* a check-up at the dentist this *morning.*

38 er

herb verb kerb here were nerve serve deserve verse fern stern never every silver sister father mother brother

1 Pass *over* the *paper* please.

2 *After winter* comes spring.

39 ow

down sown town bowl fowl howl show shower mow mower flow flown clown owner flower brown drown frown crown tow towel

1 *How* many days do we have *snow* each year?

2 An *owl* flies *low* over the ground.

42 y

duty city tidy Katy Judy study bury easy grey

1 It is a *pity* to *copy* your work.

2 The baby is *very tiny.*

43 ss

mess chess press boss moss toss ass lass brass class gloss Swiss puss

1 Please do not *fuss* about your *dress.*

2 You will be *cross* if you don't *pass.*

44 all

stall shallow allow finally usually

1 Let's play hand *ball* in the school *hall.*

2 I *shall* blow up a *balloon* for the party.

45 ell

cell dell hell yell cello hello dwell trellis fellow swell spelling excellent

1 Pick that *shell* up off the beach.

2 My favourite *jelly* is *yellow.*

46 ill

gill mill pill sill till trill thrill quill grill drill swill pillow willow illness

1 Jack and *Jill* went up the *hill.*

2 If you are *silly* that water will *spill.*

47 ing

fling sling wring doing going

1 *Bring* some *string* to tie onto the kite.

2 We *sing* carols at Christmas.

48 ong

pong prong

1 We all *belong* to the same family.

2 You are sitting in the *wrong* place.

51 silent e

can cane man mane pan pane van vane fat fate mat mate rat rate sag sage dam dame bad bade fad fade car care bar bare mar mare

1 My rag doll is the *same* as yours.

2 I wear a hat with my *cape.*

52 ate ite

fate mate rate late later plate private climate quite excite writer unite polite trite mite

1 I will *write* and *invite* you to my party.

2 I *hate* swimming in cold water.

53 ave ive

cave pave rave wave shave brave travel grave gravel crave slave haven't dive hive jive wives drive knives arrive driver river given forgive deliver motive

1 You were very *brave* to *save* your friend.

2 *I've* got to *live* in another town.

54 one

lone tone throne crone drone shone zone lonely honest telephone

1 The bees have *gone* to make *honey*.

2 Do not lift that heavy *stone alone*.

55 ake

fake rake flake brake baker stake quake

1 Help me *bake* a *cake*.

2 *Take* care not to *make* a mistake.

56 ike oke

hike spike coke choke broke broken spoke stoke

1 Have you a *smoke* alarm in your house?

2 A mountain *bike* does not look *like* a racer.

Letter Families

adgqcoe

rnmhbp

iuyjlt

vwx

fk

sz

ABCDEFGHIJKLM

NOPQRSTUVWXYZ

Handwriting Practice

a

e

i

o

u

ran   Dad

yes   bed

dig   fit

got   top

but   cup

the   and

in   with

of   by

him   come

SPELLING WORLD BOOK 1 © AMANDA GRAY / NASH POLLOCK PUBLISHING 1994

Look   Cover   Write   Check

1 Read each word. Look hard at it.
2 Cover the word with your hand and write it in the space.
3 Turn your page over. How many words can you write down?

be _be_____   the _the_____

he _he_____   was _was_____

me _me_____   you _you_____

we _we_____   your _your_____

she _she_____   and _and_____

Look at the picture. Fill in the missing words.

1 W _   can see t _ _ cat.

2 S _ _   is sitting on a box.

3 Can y _ _   see the dog?

4 H _   is peeping round the door.

5 He will b _   on the next page.

6 Tell m _   what y _ _ _   book is called.

7 Who w _ _   asleep on the box?

8 Cat a _ _   mouse are together.

The cat is asleep on the box.

Look   Cover   Write   Check

1 Read each word. Look hard at it.
2 Cover the word with your hand and write it in the space.
3 Turn your page over. How many words can you write down?

do *do*   in *in*

go *go*   is *is*

no *no*   it *it*

so *so*   if *if*

to *to*   with *with*

Handwriting Practice

do   *go*   *no*

so   *to*   *in*

is   *if*   *it*

with

Do go to see if it is in.

→

   SPELLING WORLD BOOK 1 © AMANDA GRAY / NASH POLLOCK PUBLISHING 1994

Look Cover Write Check

1 Read each word. Look hard at it.
2 Cover the word with your hand and write it in the space.
3 Turn your page over. How many words can you write down?

or *or*

on *on*

of *of*

off *off*

Mr Mr

are *are*

have *have*

by *by*

my *my*

Mrs Mrs

Branch Crossword

Across
1 Keep o _ _   the grass.
2 I h _ _ _   a new coat.
4 Put o _   your shoes.
5 My teacher is M _   Smith.
7 Come and sit b _   me.

Down
1 Here is a piece o _   paper.
3 We a _ _   going away.
4 Choose a lolly o _   an ice cream.
5 My Mum is M _ _   Jones.
6 M _   name is Tom.

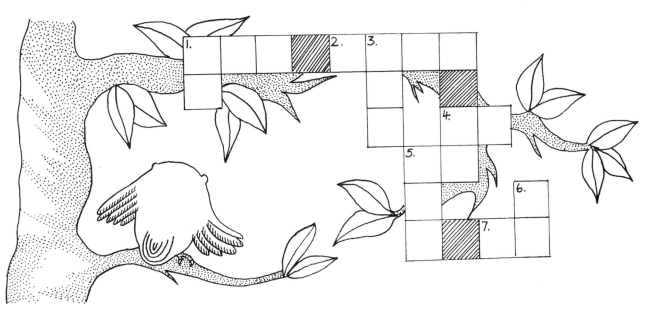

Look   Cover   Write   Check

1 Read each word. Look hard at it.
2 Cover the word with your hand and write it in the space.
3 Turn your page over. How many words can you write down?

am *am*

as *as*

at *at*

come *come*

him *him*

his *his*

has *has*

Make up **a-** and **h-** words in the ladybirds.

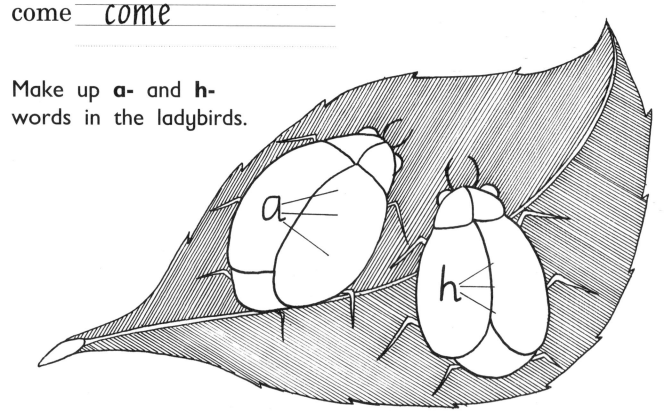

Handwriting Practice

She has come to stay at home.

→

as   has   am   him

    SPELLING WORLD BOOK 1 © AMANDA GRAY / NASH POLLOCK PUBLISHING 1994

a

1 Read each word. Look hard at it.
2 Cover the word with your hand and write it in the space.
3 Turn your page over. How many words can you write down?

bad   *bad*   cat   *cat*

had   *had*   fat   *fat*

Dad   *Dad*   hat   *hat*

can   *can*   man   *man*

ran   *ran*   bag   *bag*

Find all these words in the **Cat** wordsearch.
Write them down below the picture.

```
b a g s l f a t d n
k c a c a t l w h j
s t m a n x o d a d
h a d c t g r a n g
d c a n r m e h a t
f a n c b a d l f k
```

 e

| Look | Cover | Write | Check |

1 Read each word. Look hard at it.
2 Cover the word with your hand and write it in the space.
3 Turn your page over. How many words can you write down?

bed *bed*   men *men*

red *red*   ten *ten*

get *get*   leg *leg*

let *let*   peg *peg*

wet *wet*   yes *yes*

Choose the right spelling in each sentence.
Put a circle round the right word. Write it out again.

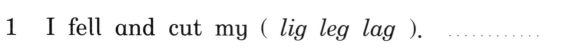

1 I fell and cut my (*lig leg lag*). ....

2 Come and (*git get*) some tea. ....

3 The (*mans menn men*) mended the road. ....

4 I am wearing my (*redd red read*) jersey. ....

5 Please (*let lett litt*) me into the house. ....

6 Put the (*pag peg pig*) on the peg board. ....

7 My teddy bear is on my (*bid bed deb*). ....

8 I got (*weet wett wet*) in the rain. ....

9 Open your eyes when you count to (*tin ten tene*).

....

   SPELLING WORLD BOOK 1 © AMANDA GRAY / NASH POLLOCK PUBLISHING 1994

i

1 Read each word. Look hard at it.
2 Cover the word with your hand and write it in the space.
3 Turn your page over. How many words can you write down?

big *big*   lip *lip*

dig *dig*   tip *tip*

did *did*   fit *fit*

hid *hid*   sit *sit*

fix *fix*   six *six*

How many words can you make from the **pig**?
Write down the words you have made.

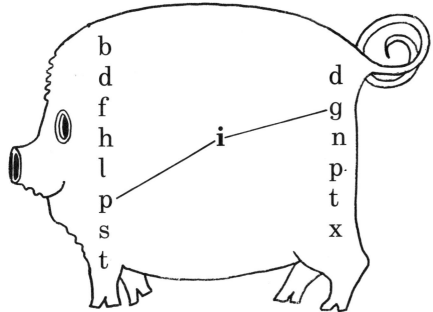

big

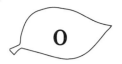

Look Cover Write Check

1 Read each word. Look hard at it.
2 Cover the word with your hand and write it in the space.
3 Turn your page over. How many words can you write down?

got   *got*

hot   *hot*

lot   *lot*

not   *not*

box   *box*

dog   *dog*

log   *log*

hop   *hop*

top   *top*

fox   *fox*

These words are mixed up.
Can you write them again in the empty leaves?

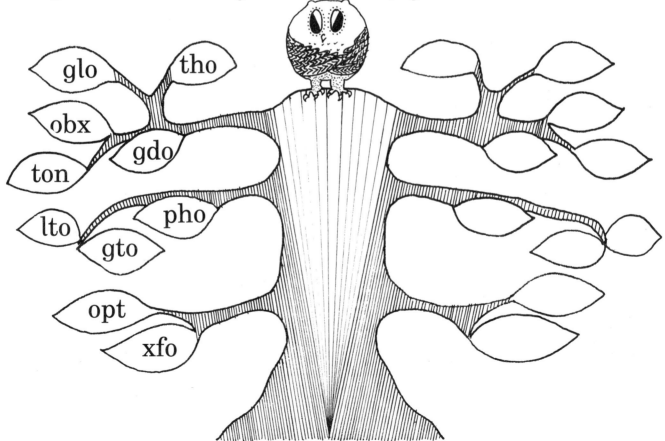

glo   tho   obx   gdo   ton   lto   pho   gto   opt   xfo

   SPELLING WORLD BOOK 1 © AMANDA GRAY / NASH POLLOCK PUBLISHING 1994

u

<table>
<tr><td colspan="4" align="center">**Look   Cover   Write   Check**</td></tr>
</table>

1 Read each word. Look hard at it.
2 Cover the word with your hand and write it in the space.
3 Turn your page over. How many words can you write down?

sun sun   **but** but

run run   **put** put

us us   **Mum** Mum

bus bus   **sum** sum

up up   **cup** cup

Handwriting Practice

sun   run   us

bus   up   cup

but   put   sum

Mum

It is fun to run in the sun.

→

Check Tree

dog	hid	of	wet	isn't	big
with	box	cup	bag	get	cat

Fill in the missing words.

1   My b _ _   is full of shopping.

2   A c _ _   chased the mice.

3   He h _ _   behind the door.

4   The circus is in the b _ _   tent.

5   He played w _ _ _   his b _ _   of bricks.

6   Tom took the d _ _   for a walk.

7   If you stand in the rain you will g _ _   w _ _   .

8   May I have a c _ _   of tea please?

9   There i _ _ ' _   any room on the bus.

 SPELLING WORLD BOOK 1 © AMANDA GRAY / NASH POLLOCK PUBLISHING 1994

Handwriting Practice

sh

st

th

ck

ch

nd

nt

wh

wash	shop
must	thing
black	stick
child	chest
wind	went
who	which

 sh

Look Cover Write Check

1 Read each word. Look hard at it.
2 Cover the word with your hand and write it in the space.
3 Turn your page over. How many words can you write down?

she _she_

fish _fish_

shed _shed_

wish _wish_

shop _shop_

dish _dish_

ship _ship_

wash _wash_

shut _shut_

push _push_

Fish Wordsearch

Write down the words that you find.

t r s h u t n w a s h g
g o w d p u s h e t r s
n d i s h p l s h e d k
s h e f s h o p f i s h
d b v w i s h s h i p c

st

Look   Cover   Write   Check

1 Read each word. Look hard at it.
2 Cover the word with your hand and write it in the space.
3 Turn your page over. How many words can you write down?

fast *fast*

last *last*

past *past*

best *best*

nest *nest*

lost *lost*

cost *cost*

post *post*

just *just*

must *must*

Join the letters from tree to tree ending in the nest.
How many words can you make? Write them down.

b
c
f
g
j
l
m
n
p
w

a
e
i
o
u

st

best

th

1 Read each word. Look hard at it.
2 Cover the word with your hand and write it in the space.
3 Turn your page over. How many words can you write down?

the the   **this** this

them them   **thin** thin

then then   **thing** thing

they they   **think** think

than than   **that** that

Handwriting Practice

The thistle is thin and thorny.

→

I think this thorn is thinner

→

than that one.

→

ck

1 Read each word. Look hard at it.
2 Cover the word with your hand and write it in the space.
3 Turn your page over. How many words can you write down?

back — *back* — pick — *pick*

black — *black* — sick — *sick*

rock — *rock* — brick — *brick*

clock — *clock* — stick — *stick*

duck — *duck* — luck — *luck*

Word Ladder

Read the clues. Change one letter on each step.

Opposite to front _____

Set of playing cards _____

Choose _____

Ill _____

Touch with your tongue _____

Chance _____

Water bird _____

back

ch | **Look   Cover   Write   Check**

1 Read each word. Look hard at it.
2 Cover the word with your hand and write it in the space.
3 Turn your page over. How many words can you write down?

chat *chat*	**chi**n *chin*
chest *chest*	**chi**p *chip*
chop *chop*	**chi**ck *chick*
rich *rich*	**chi**ld *child*
m**uch** *much*	s**uch** *such*

Chick Crossword

Across
1 Having lots of money
4 Young boy or girl
5 A friendly talk
6 Strong box
8 Fried potatoes

Down
2 It's below your mouth
3 How m _ _ _ does that book cost?
4 Young bird
5 Cut with an axe
7 These are s _ _ _ lovely flowers!

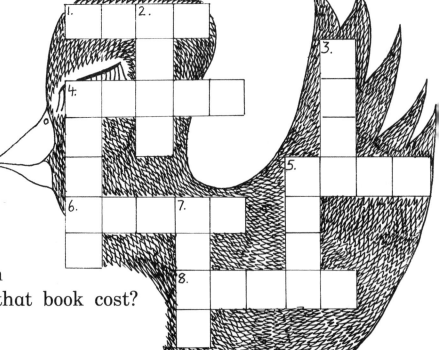

   SPELLING WORLD BOOK 1 © AMANDA GRAY / NASH POLLOCK PUBLISHING 1994

nd

| Look | Cover | Write | Check |

1 Read each word. Look hard at it.
2 Cover the word with your hand and write it in the space.
3 Turn your page over. How many words can you write down?

and _and_

hand _hand_

end _end_

send _send_

pond _pond_

find _find_

wind _wind_

mind _mind_

beh**ind** _behind_

under _under_

Look at the picture. Fill in the missing words.

1 Who is b _ _ _ _ _ the rock?
2 What is u _ _ _ _ the water?
3 The frog a _ _ the fish live in the p _ _ _ .
4 Can you f _ _ _ the tail of the fish?
5 Does the fish m _ _ _ the cat?
6 The w _ _ _ makes waves on the pond.

 **nt**

| Look | Cover | Write | Check |

1 Read each word. Look hard at it.
2 Cover the word with your hand and write it in the space.
3 Turn your page over. How many words can you write down?

ant _ant_

pant _pant_

want _want_

hint _hint_

mint _mint_

lent _tent_

tent _tent_

bent _bent_

sent _sent_

went _went_

Follow the **hints** to find your **tent**...
Change one letter each time.

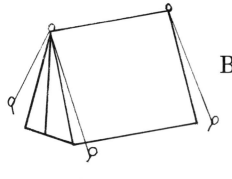

A clue to help you

Buy a p _ _ _ of milk

Breathe quickly

I w _ _ _ that!

They w _ _ _ past the house

You sleep in this when you camp outside

h _ nt

_ _ _

_ _ _

_ _ _

_ _ _

 wh

| Look | Cover | Write | Check |

1 Read each word. Look hard at it.
2 Cover the word with your hand and write it in the space.
3 Turn your page over. How many words can you write down?

who *who*   **wha**t *what*

whose *whose*   **why** *why*

where *where*   **which** *which*

when *when*   **whi**le *while*

wheel *wheel*   **whi**te *white*

The **wh** Puzzle

WHITE ST.

JONES BUTCHER

Use the picture to find the answers.

1 _ _ _   did the robbery?

2 _ _ _ _ _ _   did it take place?

3 _ _ _ _   time did it happen?

4 _ _ _   saw it happen?

5 _ _ _ _ _   street did he run down?

6 _ _ _   owns the dogs?

7 _ _ _ _ _ _   van can you see?

8 _ _ _ _   the robber is caught, _ _ _ _ _ _   will
   he be taken?

Check Tree

this	fast	shop	shut	chips	lent	under
when	child	went	that	cost	pick	hand

Fill in the missing words from the boxes.

1 W _ _ _   you leave, please s _ _ _   the door.

2 The train went f _ _ _   along the track.

3 T _ _ _   book belongs on t _ _ _   shelf.

4 Go and buy some fish and c _ _ _ _ .

5 The little c _ _ _ _   plays with her toys.

6 I am going to the sweet s _ _ _ .

7 Don't p _ _ _   the flowers!

8 Moles live u _ _ _ _   the ground.

9 I w _ _ _   to school and l _ _ _   my book to Annie.

10 Hold my h _ _ _   when we cross the road.

11 My coat c _ _ _   a lot of money.

   SPELLING WORLD BOOK 1 © AMANDA GRAY / NASH POLLOCK PUBLISHING 1994

Handwriting Practice

y

ay

oo

ee

ar

or

er

ow

cry   fly

yesterday

zoo   week

street   dark

morning   winter

other   own

 y

Look Cover Write Check

1 Read each word. Look hard at it.
2 Cover the word with your hand and write it in the space.
3 Turn your page over. How many words can you write down?

by _by_   boy _boy_

my _my_   toy _toy_

fly _fly_   buy _buy_

sky _sky_   cry _cry_

why _why_   try _try_

Y Crossword

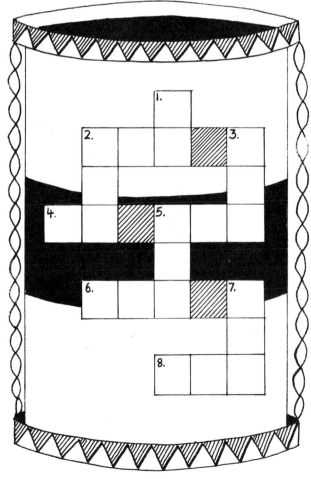

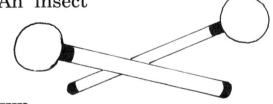

Across
2 Male child
4 Near
5 Something to play with
6 Weep
8 An insect

Down
1 Belonging to me
2 Pay for something
3 The air above
5 Make an effort
7 For what reason?

  SPELLING WORLD BOOK 1 © AMANDA GRAY / NASH POLLOCK PUBLISHING 1994

 ay

| **Look** | **Cover** | **Write** | **Check** |

1 Read each word. Look hard at it.
2 Cover the word with your hand and write it in the space.
3 Turn your page over. How many words can you write down?

may	*may*	way	*way*
say	*say*	away	*away*
day	*day*	play	*play*
today	*today*	stay	*stay*
yesterday	*yesterday*		

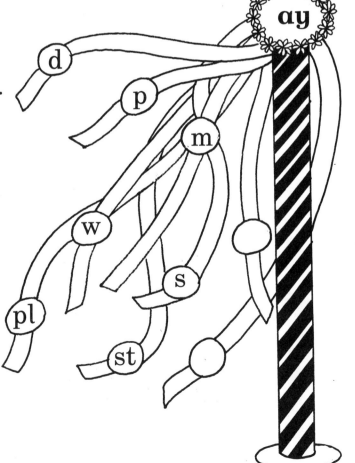

Play with **ay** today.

How many words can you make?

Can you make any **ay** words with new letters?

Look Cover Write Check

1 Read each word. Look hard at it.
2 Cover the word with your hand and write it in the space.
3 Turn your page over. How many words can you write down?

book   *book*

look   *look*

took   *took*

door   *door*

poor   *poor*

food   *food*

good   *good*

wood   *wood*

zoo   *zoo*

too   *too*

Handwriting Practice

Robin Hood took a good look at

→

a cook book. He took some wood to

→

make a fire, and took some sticks too.

→

SPELLING WORLD BOOK 1 © AMANDA GRAY / NASH POLLOCK PUBLISHING 1994

 **ee**

1 Read each word. Look hard at it.
2 Cover the word with your hand and write it in the space.
3 Turn your page over. How many words can you write down?

see _see_   meet _meet_

tree _tree_   feet _feet_

three _three_   sweet _sweet_

week _week_   sheet _sheet_

cheek _cheek_   street _street_

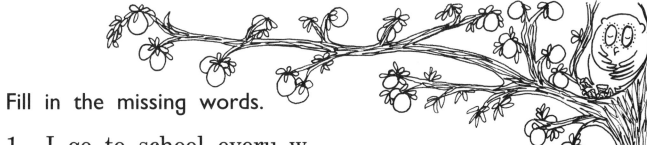

Fill in the missing words.

1 I go to school every w _ _ _ .
2 A triangle has t _ _ _ _ sides.
3 Can you s _ _ my sw _ _ _ packet?
4 My f _ _ _ are too big for my shoes.
5 We m _ _ _ our friends in the st _ _ _ _ .
6 I'm going to buy a sh _ _ _ of stickers.
7 My c _ _ _ _ is below my eye.
8 There is an apple t _ _ _ in the garden.

 **ar**

1 Read each word. Look hard at it.
2 Cover the word with your hand and write it in the space.
3 Turn your page over. How many words can you write down?

c**ar** *car*

c**ar**d *card*

f**ar** *far*

f**ar**m *farm*

arm *arm*

b**ar**k *bark*

d**ar**k *dark*

p**ar**k *park*

st**ar** *star*

w**ar** *war*

How many words can you make? Write them down.

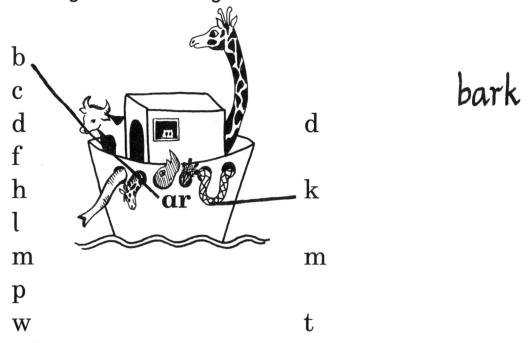

bark

          SPELLING WORLD BOOK 1 © AMANDA GRAY / NASH POLLOCK PUBLISHING 1994

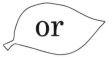 **or**

1 Read each word. Look hard at it.
2 Cover the word with your hand and write it in the space.
3 Turn your page over. How many words can you write down?

for _for_   born _born_

fort _fort_   worn _worn_

sort _sort_   corn _corn_

short _short_   corner _corner_

story _story_   morning _____

Fort Wordsearch

Search across and down.

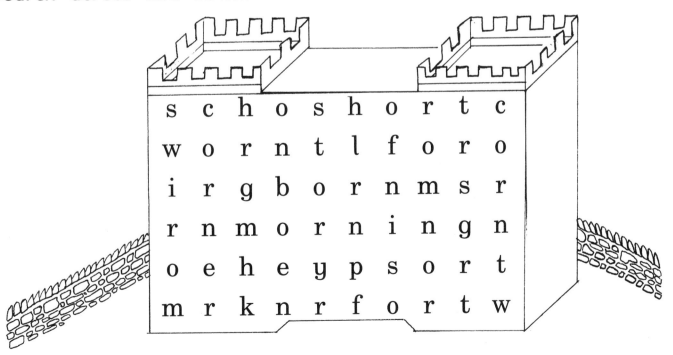

s	c	h	o	s	h	o	r	t	c
w	o	r	n	t	l	f	o	r	o
i	r	g	b	o	r	n	m	s	r
r	n	m	o	r	n	i	n	g	n
o	e	h	e	y	p	s	o	r	t
m	r	k	n	r	f	o	r	t	w

Write down the words that you find.

er

Look Cover Write Check

1 Read each word. Look hard at it.
2 Cover the word with your hand and write it in the space.
3 Turn your page over. How many words can you write down?

her _her_   wa**ter** _water_

ot**her** _other_   la**ter** _later_

ov**er** _over_   af**ter** _after_

und**er** _under_   win**ter** _winter_

pap**er** _paper_   summ**er** _summer_

Complete this poem

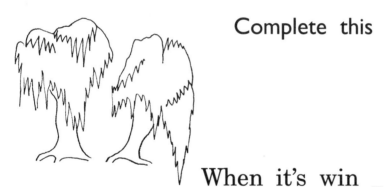

When it's win _ _ _
The weath _ _
Gets co _ _ _ _ .
La _ _ _ ,
In s _ _ _ _ _ ,
It's war _ _ _
O _ _ _ and u _ _ _ _
The wa _ _ _ .

    SPELLING WORLD BOOK 1 © AMANDA GRAY / NASH POLLOCK PUBLISHING 1994

 **ow**

1 Read each word. Look hard at it.
2 Cover the word with your hand and write it in the space.
3 Turn your page over. How many words can you write down?

bow   bow   cow   cow

how   how   now   now

sow   sow   snow   snow

owl   owl   low   low

own   own   slow   slow

The Great Owl Hunt

How many other words with **ow** do you know?
Write them on the page.

look in reading books, dictionaries, wall charts

Check Tree

buy	stay	sky	story	poor	fly
yard	owl	morning	are	zoo	dark
slowly	low	summer	see	after	three
farm	weeks	other	away	took	stars

Fill in the missing words from the list.

1 I will f _ _   my kite in the s _ _ .

2 Sam and Ranju are in the t _ _ _ _ -legged race.

3 The st _ _ _   shine in the d _ _ _ .

4 Please read a st _ _ _   this m _ _ _ _ _ _ _ .

5 We shall s _ _   the tigers at the z _ _ .

6 There a _ _   four w _ _ _ _   in each month.

7 Let's b _ _   some crisps today.

8 Don't take this one. Take the o _ _ _ _   one.

9 At night the o _ _   flies sl _ _ _ _   over the
   l _ _ houses.

10 You can s _ _ _   a _ _ _   from school if
    you are ill.

11 The cows are in the f _ _ _   y _ _ _ .

12 Af _ _ _   su _ _ _ _   we have autumn.

13 Robin Hood t _ _ _   money from the rich
    for the p _ _ _ .

   SPELLING WORLD BOOK 1 © AMANDA GRAY / NASH POLLOCK PUBLISHING 1994

Handwriting Practice

y

ss

all

ell

ill

ing

ong

every   baby

grass   less

small   wall

shell   bell

silly   Jill

spring   swing

among   long

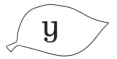

Look Cover Write Check

1 Read each word. Look hard at it.
2 Cover the word with your hand and write it in the space.
3 Turn your page over. How many words can you write down?

any *any*

many *many*

ba**by** *baby*

la**dy** *lady*

bo**dy** *body*

very *very*

ev**ery** *every*

pity *pity*

tiny *tiny*

cop**y** *copy*

Baby Crossword

Across
   2 Grown-up woman
   3 Very young child
   6 Your writing is v _ _ _ neat
   8 Please c _ _ _ these patterns
  10 Have you a _ _ food?

Down
   1 Lots of
   4 Your head, arms and legs are
      attached to it
   5 Very small
   7 Each, all
   9 Be sorry for someone

SPELLING WORLD BOOK 1 © AMANDA GRAY / NASH POLLOCK PUBLISHING 1994

SS

Look	Cover	Write	Check

1 Read each word. Look hard at it.
2 Cover the word with your hand and write it in the space.
3 Turn your page over. How many words can you write down?

pass *pass*

mass *mass*

grass *grass*

less *less*

dress *dress*

miss *miss*

hiss *hiss*

loss *loss*

cross *cross*

fuss *fuss*

The **ss** word ladder

Change one letter in each word.

put clothes on

mustard and c _ _ _ _ _

angry

fat and ugly

it grows on lawns

you get it in windows

your form in school

d	r		s	s
g				

 **all**

Look Cover Write Check

1 Read each word. Look hard at it.
2 Cover the word with your hand and write it in the space.
3 Turn your page over. How many words can you write down?

all   *all*

ball   *ball*

balloon   *balloon*

hall   *hall*

shall   *shall*

call   *call*

fall   *fall*

tall   *tall*

wall   *wall*

small   *small*

Balloon Wordsearch

Write down all the words you can find.

```
b  w  a  l  l  s
a  c  n  t  a  h
l  l  e  s  n  a
l  w  a  h  i  l
o  s  m  a  l  l
o  d  c  l  a  r
n  b  a  l  l  h
a  f  l  a  g  n
f  a  l  l  t  a
k  r  a  l  a  r
g  s  t  a  l  l
a  q  p  l  l  n
```

   SPELLING WORLD BOOK 1 © AMANDA GRAY / NASH POLLOCK PUBLISHING 1994

ell

Look   Cover   Write   Check

1   Read each word. Look hard at it.
2   Cover the word with your hand and write it in the space.
3   Turn your page over. How many words can you write down?

bell   *bell*

fell   *fell*

sell   *sell*

tell   *tell*

well   *well*

shell   *shell*

smell   *smell*

spell   *spell*

jelly   *jelly*

yellow   *yellow*

Write a short story about this picture.
How many words from the list can you use?

 **ill**

| **Look** | **Cover** | **Write** | **Check** |

1 Read each word. Look hard at it.
2 Cover the word with your hand and write it in the space.
3 Turn your page over. How many words can you write down?

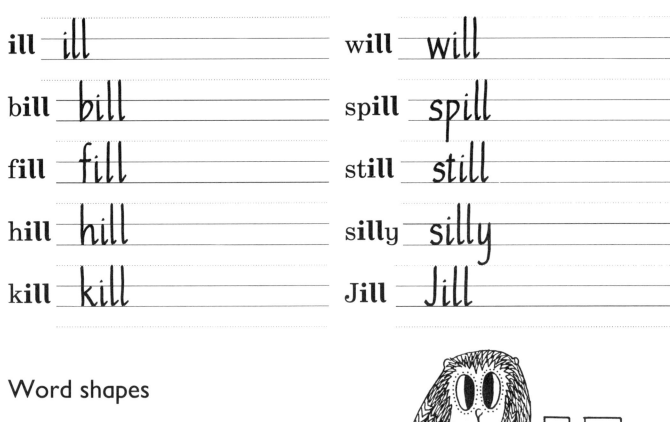

ill _ill_   **will** _will_

bill _bill_   **spill** _spill_

fill _fill_   **still** _still_

hill _hill_   **silly** _silly_

kill _kill_   **Jill** _Jill_

Word shapes

Fill in the shapes with **-ill** words.

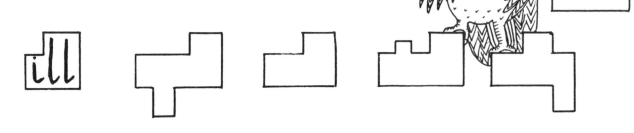

Make some word shapes for a friend.

   SPELLING WORLD BOOK 1 © AMANDA GRAY / NASH POLLOCK PUBLISHING 1994

 **ing**

1 Read each word. Look hard at it.
2 Cover the word with your hand and write it in the space.
3 Turn your page over. How many words can you write down?

r**ing** _ring_   w**ing** _wing_

br**ing** _bring_   sw**ing** _swing_

spr**ing** _spring_   s**ing** _sing_

str**ing** _string_   k**ing** _king_

th**ing** _thing_   st**ing** _sting_

Handwriting Practice

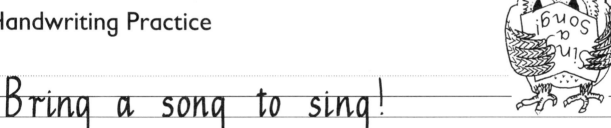

Bring a song to sing!

→

Mend the wing with some string.

→

The king swings in spring.

→

 **ong**

1 Read each word. Look hard at it.
2 Cover the word with your hand and write it in the space.
3 Turn your page over. How many words can you write down?

song *song*   long *long*

strong *strong*   along *along*

belong *belong*   among *among*

wrong *wrong*   gong *gong*

Choose the right spelling in each sentence.
Cross out the wrong words. Write out the right one.

1 We will sing a (*snog sond song*) together. ....

2 Come (*allon along allong*) to my party. ....

3 Find the right spelling (*among ammung amung*)
these words. ....

4 I (*bellong delog belong*) to my family. ....

5 Is this string (*strog strong srong*) enough? ....

6 How (*log lon long*) is your hair? ....

7 Is this right or is it (*rong wrong wrog*)? ....

Check Tree

sing	tiny	spell	Jill	tell	dress	shall
many	small	cross	strong	spring	hill	gong

Fill in the missing words from the boxes.

1 The Borrowers are t _ _ _ people.

2 A man who can lift an elephant must

be s _ _ _ _ _ !

3 Why are you c _ _ _ _ with me?

4 We s _ _ _ _ have tea at three o'clock.

5 T _ _ _ me a story about yourself.

6 Jack and J _ _ _ went up the h _ _ _ .

7 How m _ _ _ people are in your family?

8 She is wearing her best d _ _ _ _ .

9 Make a s _ _ _ _ with a magic wand.

10 The birds s _ _ _ in s _ _ _ _ _ .

11 Are you as s _ _ _ _ as the Borrowers?

12 Bang the g _ _ _ for dinner time.

Handwriting Practice

e   e

ate

ite

ave

ive

one

ake

ike

oke

made   date

bite   brave

done   honey

mistake   strike

smoke   invite

        SPELLING WORLD BOOK 1 © AMANDA GRAY / NASH POLLOCK PUBLISHING 1994

silent e

| Look | Cover | Write | Check |

1 Read each word. Look hard at it.
2 Cover the word with your hand and write it in the space.
3 Turn your page over. How many words can you write down?

mad _mad_   made _made_

cap _cap_   cape _cape_

hat _hat_   hate _hate_

Sam _Sam_   same _same_

rag _rag_   rage _rage_

Handwriting Practice

I hate wearing this stupid hat.

→

Sam got mad when he was made

→

the same. Tape that dripping tap!

→

1 Read each word. Look hard at it.
2 Cover the word with your hand and write it in the space.
3 Turn your page over. How many words can you write down?

ate *ate*	**bite** *bite*
date *date*	**kite** *kite*
gate *gate*	**white** *white*
hate *hate*	**write** *write*
water *water*	**invite** *invite*

Join the ribbon letters to the **ate** or **ite** on the k**ite**.
How many words can you make? Write them down.

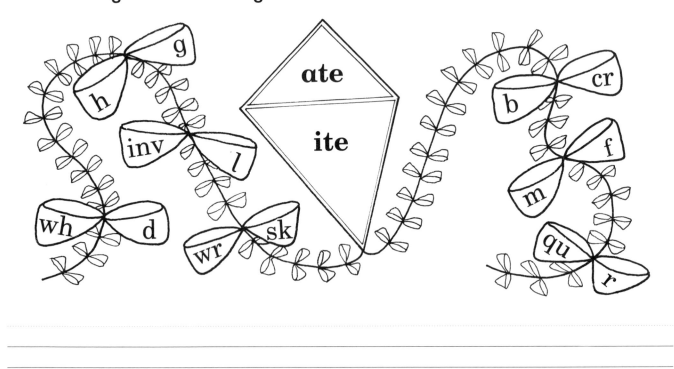

ave

 ive

1 Read each word. Look hard at it.
2 Cover the word with your hand and write it in the space.
3 Turn your page over. How many words can you write down?

g**ave**	*gave*	g**ive**	*give*
h**ave**	*have*	l**ive**	*live*
br**ave**	*brave*	al**ive**	*alive*
beh**ave**	*behave*	f**ive**	*five*
s**ave**	*save*	**I've**	*I've*

Choose the right spelling in each sentence.
Put a circle round the right word. Write it out again.

1 If you (*giv give gif*) her a present, you will
(*hav have hev*) to wrap it up. ....

2 I (*liv live lev*) at Number (*fiv fife five*),
Lower Lane. ....

3 We must (*sive save sayve*) the trees in the
rain forest. ....

4 (*Ive I've Eive*) been told to (*behayve beheve*
behave) myself. ....

5 You were very (*breve brafe brave*) when the doctor
(*gaf geve gave*) you the medicine. ....

 one

1 Read each word. Look hard at it.
2 Cover the word with your hand and write it in the space.
3 Turn your page over. How many words can you write down?

one   *one*   a**lone** *alone*

b**one**   *bone*   **money** *money*

c**one**   *cone*   **honey** *honey*

d**one**   *done*   st**one** *stone*

g**one**   *gone*   n**one**   *none*

Cone Wordsearch

Write down the words that you find. _____

```
      c
   d  o w
 n o n e s
 h n e o t
 o e t n o
 h s b e n
a e m o n e y
l y t n s q o
o k o e c e d
n p n g o n e
e w e c n t p
t h r o n e x l e
```

 **ake**

1 Read each word. Look hard at it.
2 Cover the word with your hand and write it in the space.
3 Turn your page over. How many words can you write down?

m**ake** _make_   t**ake** _take_

w**ake** _wake_   sh**ake** _shake_

aw**ake** _awake_   sn**ake** _snake_

b**ake** _bake_   l**ake** _lake_

c**ake** _cake_   mist**ake**

Bake a **Cake** Crossword

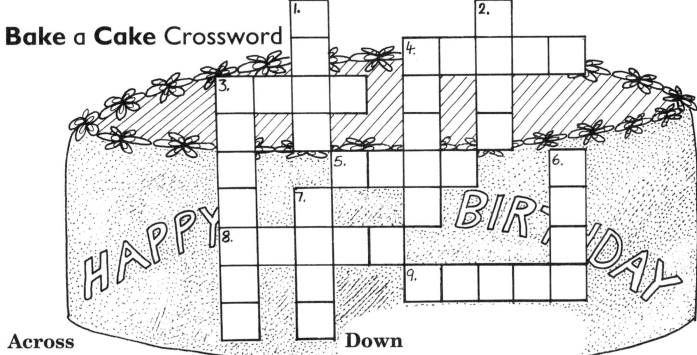

Across
3 Produce something
4 Poisonous animal without legs!
5 Carry away
8 Not asleep
9 Snow _ _ _ _ _

Down
1 Eat this for tea
2 Stop sleeping
3 Something you've done wrong
4 Tremble
6 Cook in an oven
7 Large pond (or small sea?)

 **ike**

 oke

1 Read each word. Look hard at it.
2 Cover the word with your hand and write it in the space.
3 Turn your page over. How many words can you write down?

b**ike**	*bike*	**joke**	*joke*
l**ike**	*like*	p**oke**	*poke*
a**like**	*alike*	w**oke**	*woke*
str**ike**	*strike*	sm**oke**	*smoke*
p**ike**	*pike*		

Match the meanings to the words.

Looking like one another ....

Comes out of chimney ....

Be friendly with someone ....

Fierce fish ....

Bicycle ....

Push at something with your finger ....

Hit, attack suddenly ....

Stopped sleeping ....

Something funny ....

Check Tree

have	stone	mistake	bike	hate	make
strike	write	poke	hat	invite	take
live	mad	honey	cake	date	made

Fill in the missing words from the list.

1 I h _ _ _ wearing this school h _ _ .

2 Are you m _ _ because I m _ _ _ you clear up this mess?

3 What is the d _ _ _ of your birthday?

4 I am going to w _ _ _ _ and i _ _ _ _ _ you to my party.

5 H _ _ _ a go!

6 Which house do you l _ _ _ in?

7 Bees make h _ _ _ _ .

8 Castles and churches are made of s _ _ _ _ .

9 When you bake the c _ _ _ , don't make a m _ _ _ _ _ _ !

10 How long did it t _ _ _ you to m _ _ _ that model?

11 Have you learned to ride a b _ _ _ ?

12 If I p _ _ _ that snake it might str _ _ _ at me with its fangs.

Handwriting Practice

one	two
three	four
five	six
seven	eight
nine	ten
red	blue
black	brown
green	pink
white	purple
yellow	orange
Sunday	Monday
Tuesday	Wednesday
Thursday	Friday
Saturday	

 SPELLING WORLD BOOK 1 © AMANDA GRAY / NASH POLLOCK PUBLISHING 1994

 Days

1 Read each word. Look hard at it.
2 Cover the word with your hand and write it in the space.
3 Turn your page over. How many words can you write down?

Sun**day** _Sunday_

Mon**day** _Monday_

Tues**day** _Tuesday_

Wednes**day** _Wednesday_

Thurs**day** _Thursday_

Fri**day** _Friday_

Satur**day** _Saturday_

Make your own calendar.

Sunday					

Number Tree

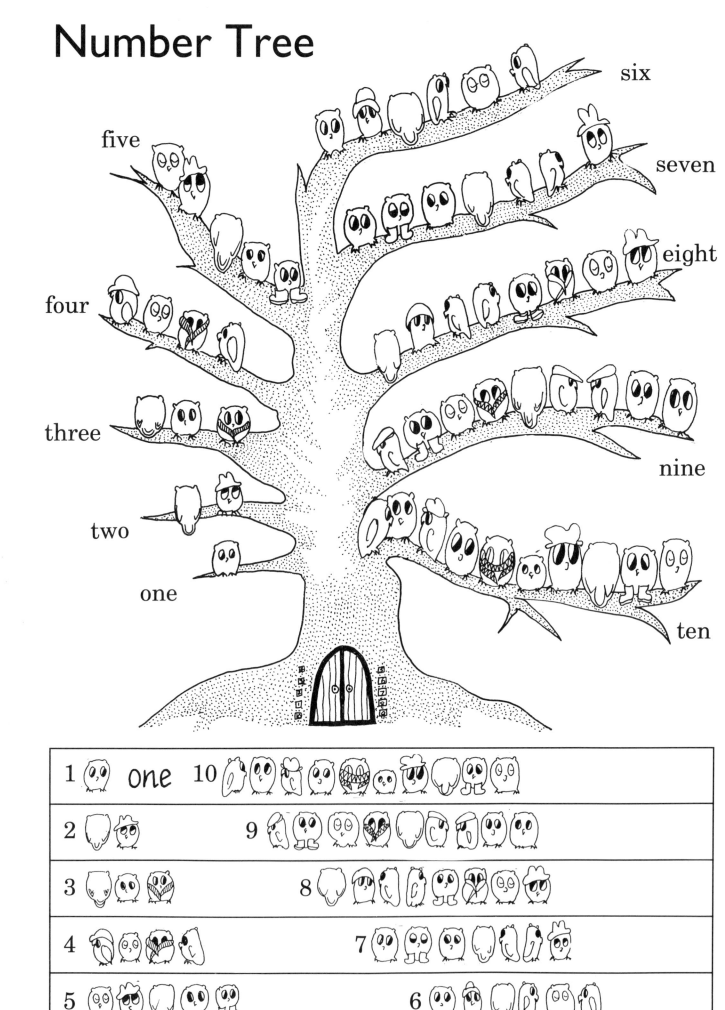

Colours

Look   Cover   Write   Check

1 Read each word. Look hard at it.
2 Cover the word with your hand and write it in the space.
3 Turn your page over. How many words can you write down?

red *red*

blue *blue*

black *black*

brown *brown*

green *green*

pink *pink*

white *white*

purple *purple*

yellow *yellow*

orange *orange*

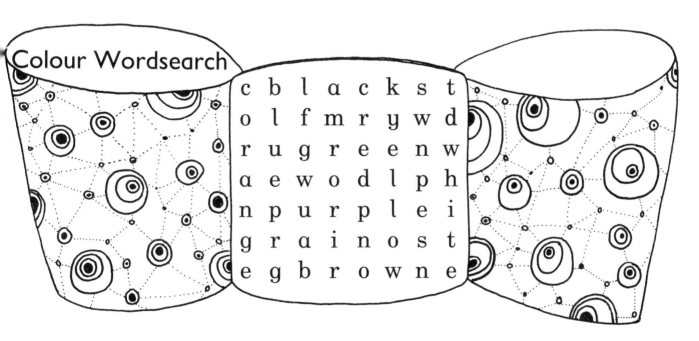

Colour Wordsearch

```
c b l a c k s t
o l f m r y w d
r u g r e e n w
a e w o d l p h
n p u r p l e i
g r a i n o s t
e g b r o w n e
```

Write down the words you find.

Test 1 pages 10-37

The underlined words have been spelled wrong!
Write out the correct spelling.

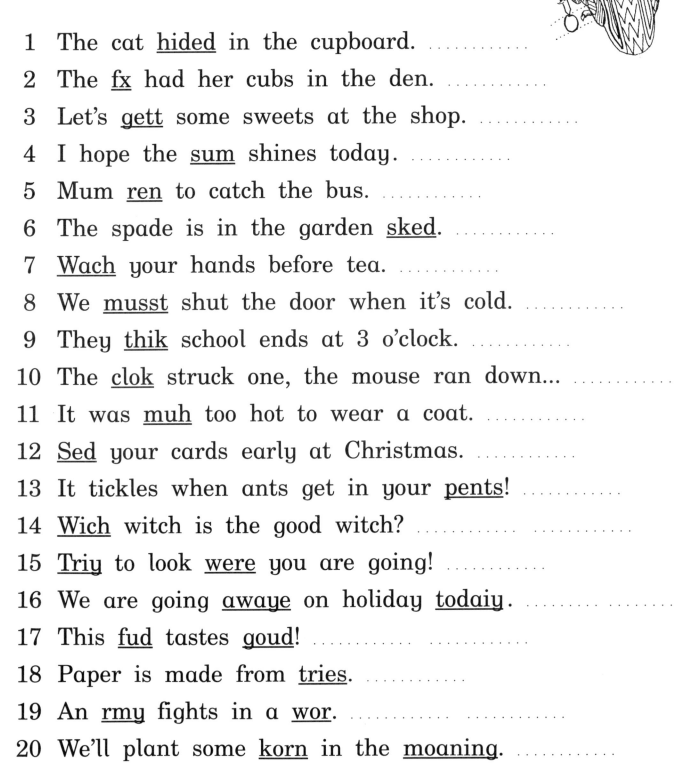

1 The cat <u>hided</u> in the cupboard. . . . .

2 The <u>fx</u> had her cubs in the den. . . . .

3 Let's <u>gett</u> some sweets at the shop. . . . .

4 I hope the <u>sum</u> shines today. . . . .

5 Mum <u>ren</u> to catch the bus. . . . .

6 The spade is in the garden <u>sked</u>. . . . .

7 <u>Wach</u> your hands before tea. . . . .

8 We <u>musst</u> shut the door when it's cold. . . . .

9 They <u>thik</u> school ends at 3 o'clock. . . . .

10 The <u>clok</u> struck one, the mouse ran down... . . . .

11 It was <u>muh</u> too hot to wear a coat. . . . .

12 <u>Sed</u> your cards early at Christmas. . . . .

13 It tickles when ants get in your <u>pents</u>! . . . .

14 <u>Wich</u> witch is the good witch? . . . .

15 <u>Triy</u> to look <u>were</u> you are going! . . . .

16 We are going <u>awaye</u> on holiday <u>todaiy</u>. . . . .

17 This <u>fud</u> tastes <u>goud</u>! . . . .

18 Paper is made from <u>tries</u>. . . . .

19 An <u>rmy</u> fights in a <u>wor</u>. . . . .

20 We'll plant some <u>korn</u> in the <u>moaning</u>. . . . .

. . . .

 SPELLING WORLD BOOK 1 © AMANDA GRAY / NASH POLLOCK PUBLISHING 1994

Test 2 pages 38-61

The <u>underlined</u> words have been spelled wrong!
Write out the correct spelling.

1 Cross <u>ova</u> the bridge to the <u>uvver</u> side. ....

2 You need your <u>oan</u> pencil ....

3 If you <u>coppy</u> me, you will learn to write. ....

4 Which <u>clas</u> are you in at school? ....

5 The <u>warl</u> is too high to climb over. ....

6 Can you <u>smel</u> the lunch cooking? ....

7 If you step on the spider you will <u>kille</u> it. ....

8 <u>Brig</u> your swimming things when you come. ....

9 Listen to the bird <u>sonk</u>. ....

10 Your Mum will be in a <u>raige</u> if you wear
    that rag! ....

11 You'll <u>hait</u> doing that washing. ....

12 They <u>gav</u> blood to <u>saive</u> lives. ....

13 We've eaten all the eggs – there are <u>nun</u> left. ....

14 I stayed <u>awak</u> all night. ....

15 Listen to the clock <u>stirke</u> twelve. ....

16 <u>Blak</u> and <u>wite</u> make grey. ....

17 After <u>Wensday</u> comes <u>Turssday</u>. ....

18 There are 52 <u>weks</u> in a year. ....

19 <u>Niyn</u> and <u>wun</u> make ten. ....

20 There are <u>fife</u> fingers on each hand. ....

pupil names	9 Handwriting 1	10 Handwriting 2	11 First words 1	12 First words 2	13 First words 3	14 First words 4	15 a	16 e	17 i	18 o	19 u	20 Check Tree 1	21 Handwriting 3	22 sh	23 st	24 th	25 ck	26 ch	27 nd	28 nt	29 wh	30 Check Tree 2	31 Handwriting 4	32 y	33 ay